Creativ Journal:

MW00620466

Faith Inspired Writing Prompts & Hope-Filled Poetry

scribble your name:

Address:

Date: Finished:

Journaling Scribbles Collection

An artist's & writer's

c o p y r i g h t

encourages a culture of support

and honors the person

who creates, writes, & designs

publications & works of art.

Thank you for not copying without permission.

Cover design, artwork, and interior formatting by Patricia Tiffany Morris, owner of Tiffany Inks Studio LLC.

Scripture quotations from The Authorized (King James) Version. Rights in the Authorized Version in the United Kingdom are vested in the Crown. Reproduced by permission of the Crown's patentee, Cambridge University Press.

Other requests please contact:

Tiffany Inks Studio LLC
PO Box 299
Bondurant, IA 50035

ISBN: 978-1-955274-11-1

www.patriciatiffanymorris.com

Endorsements:

"An inspiration station for contemplators, doodlers, journalers, planners, dreamers, and creatives of many kinds who want to renew thoughts and cultivate gratitude in a hands-on way. Patricia inspires and guides with a variety of ways to combine art, bible study, prayer, contemplation, dreaming, and goal setting all based on Philippians 4:8.

I particularly love that she's provided a little help for those who are just getting started with adding lettering and drawing in their spiritual practice."

~Ginger Harrington : Author of **Holy in the Moment** (GingerHarrington.com)

"With breathtaking beauty, Patricia Tiffany Morris has created page after page of prompts that invite you to open your mind and pour out, gather, and organize thoughts, plans, feelings, and details of your life. The stunning pages in Journaling Scribbles elevate my mind-musings to a whole new level that compliments the busy neurology going on, even in my dreams.

Studies show the act of writing, gripping a utensil, and tapping into our inner world, spilling out our thoughts, activates parts of our brain that reduce stress, increases wellbeing, organizes the chaos of uncertainty, and increases our ability to reach our goals.

What an incredibly beautiful way Patricia Tiffany Morris has created to help us "mind-map" what we think... and show us who we are. My thoughts never looked so good! What a wonderful thing to pick these books up in years to come and say, "Yes, that was me!"

~Deborah McCormick Maxey, PhD: Licensed Professional Counselor, Licensed Marriage and Family Therapist , and Author of **The Endling** (DeborahMaxey.com/books)

"If you are looking for something to jumpstart your journaling process, Patricia Tiffany Morris has the answer in this series of journals. Beautifully illustrated with Patricia's own art, you're sure to discover a creative way to organize and process your busy days in a way that fits your lifestyle."

~Mary Potter Kenyon : Program Coordinator for Shalom Spirituality Center, certified grief counselor, Therapeutic Art Coach, and author of seven books, including **Called to Be Creative:** A Guide to Reigniting Your Creativity (MaryPotterKenyon.com)

"As you open this book you realize; each page is an invitation to dance. Patricia Tiffany Morris is a wonder. Since the moment we met, I've been constantly astounded by her capacity to pour out her zeal to encourage and build others up. Some might be content to create whimsical and inspiring art, and stunningly beautiful poetry and prose, then sit back and enjoy the accolades and awards that go along with it.

Not Patricia. Sure, she's got those too. But she's busily passing out keys to the Kingdom in every way she can, that our own art, writing, and our relationship with Jesus, might flourish. Social media trainings. Tech trainings. Biblical devotionals. Now, her creativity and planning journals, diaries, & sketchbooks.

I strongly recommend you snap up an armful for all the dreamers and the doers in your life. And for all you artists, here's the really unique thing about these journals: Patricia knows how the creative mind works and celebrates it! Well done, Patricia."

~Wendy Hibbard : Founder, The Writing Room and SHP Coaching; Editor, **Beneath the Mask:** Faith, Hope & Transformation in the Face of COVID-19 (wendyhibbard.com)

to the One who created all things and for His glory.

Patricia Tiffany Morris
Tiffany Inks Studio LLC

www.pinterest.com/patriciatiffanymorris.com
https://www.youtube.com/c/PatriciaTiffanyMorris
www.instagram.com/PatriciaTiffanyMorris/

Thanks!

Special appreciation to my endearing husband who offers his humor, puns, encouragement, and keen poetic insights.

To Terha Knittel, lovely composer and vocalist extraordinaire, who composed the music in the video promotions and for my book trailers.

To Kyle Knittel who guided me through many hours of video production.

To Erica Alexander who formatted my original 3D covers.

To Rachael Colby who spent long hours reminding me that I can't give up.

To Elaine Giles and the MacBytes crew for teaching me about Affinity software, Scrivener, and many, many tech tricks.

To KG Fonts and FontSpring for the stress free licenses.

To my launch team and FB group who helped proofread, edit, and cheer me toward and through publication. My gratitude to these idea generators, amazing brainstorming networkers, and the many cheerleaders, formatting ninjas, and "let-it-be-enough" believers, trust-soldiers, and prayer warriors.

to the One who created all things and for His glory.

Color, scribble, sketch, draw, & write ideas on the following pages.

Table of Contents

COLORING & DOODLING PAGE

color & doodle

add colors & textures & lines & scribbles

find your inner artist

draw & design your own doodles

artsy trees

draw a tree in fall

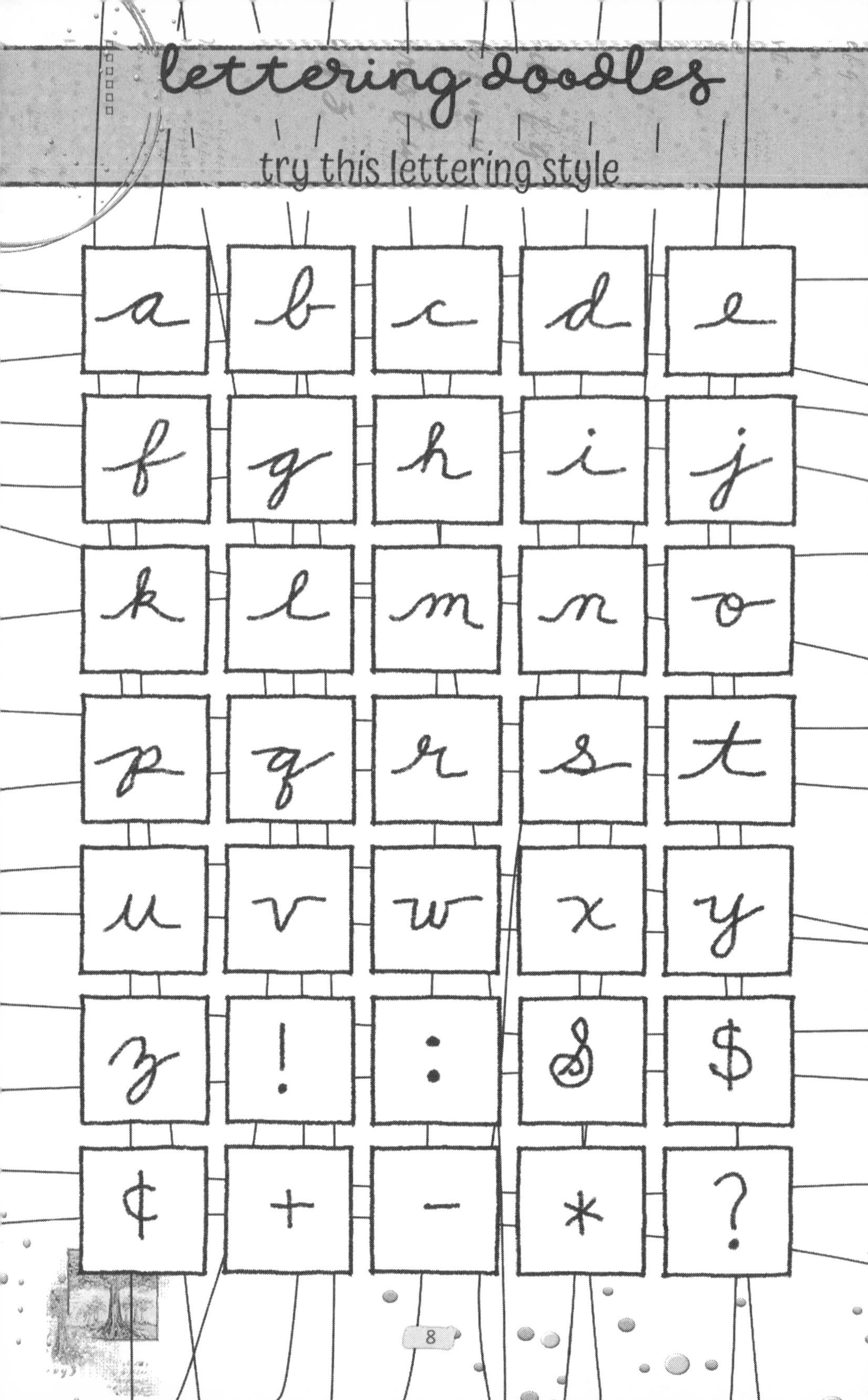
lettering doodles
try this lettering style
a
b
c
d
e
f
g
h
i
j
k
l
m
n
o
p
q
r
s
t
u
v
w
x
y
z
!
:
S
$
¢
+
-
*
?

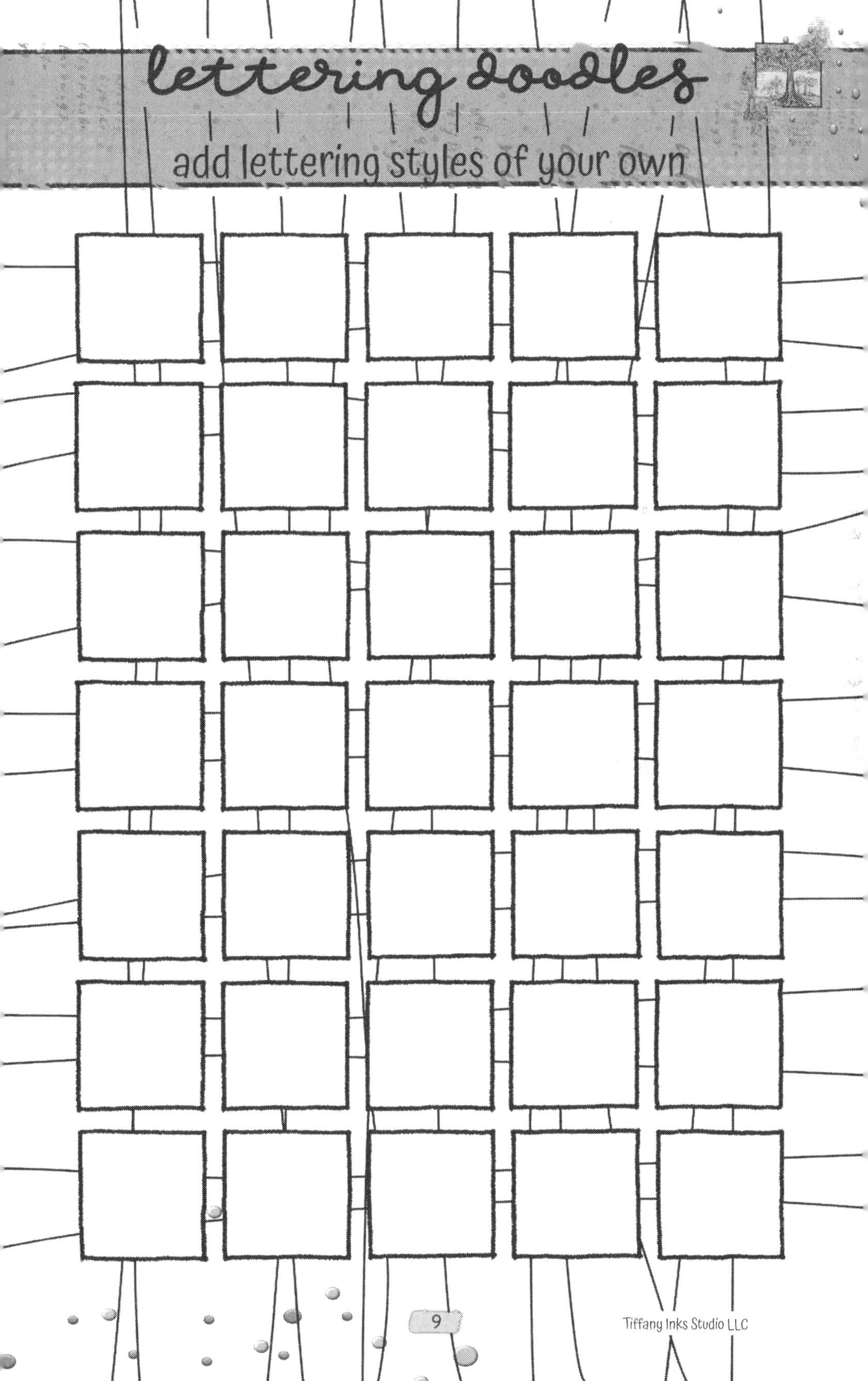
lettering doodles
add lettering styles of your own

Ideas to Use this Journal

Each section of this journal includes a poem to read and reflect upon. Enjoy the writing prompts following each inspirational poem.

The poets, musicians, and writers included a biography and links where you can find more of their work.

Check Out Other Opportunities to Write Poetry!

Dear Reader,

Thanks for purchasing this journal. While you read the poetry and journal your thoughts and record your reflections, remember to research and enjoy the art of learning. This collaboration of writers and poets does not claim to have studied extensively on the various forms and styles and poetic devices. In fact, we may not have each form properly identified because we are students ourselves. Let this humble admission be your encouragement to try different styles and forms and to continue learning and growing in your knowledge and experience or the growing list of poetry forms.

Blessings to each of you as you pursue your dreams.

Sincerely,

Patricia Tiffany Morris

And the Journaling Scribbles writers

Journaling Prompts at a Glance

Each poem includes a set of questions and writing prompts based on the poem's message, the poetic devices, or forms.

Creative Writing Journal At a Glance

Poetry Form & Resources Page Spreads

Highlighted Poem Page Spread

Questions and Journal Prompts Pages

Doodling Pages

Author Biographies and Contacts

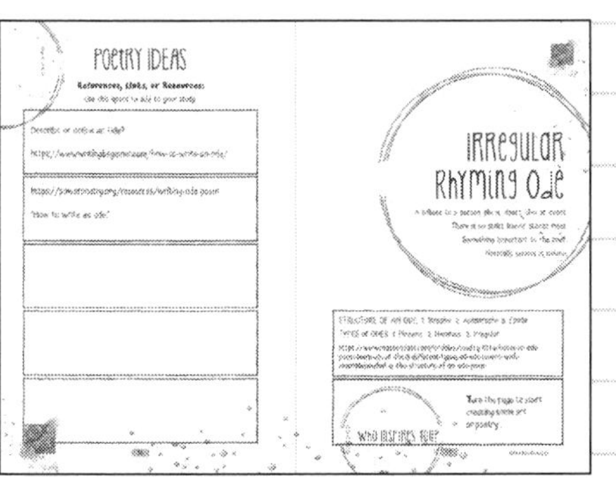

Poetry Forms & Resources Page Spread

Poetry Inspiration Page Spreads Pages

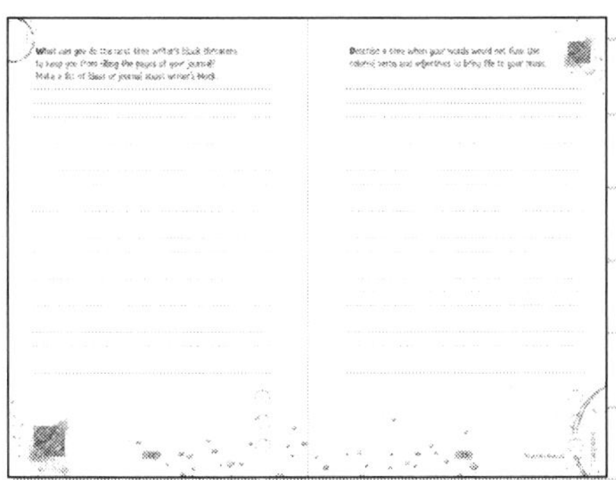

Questions & Journal Prompts Page Spread

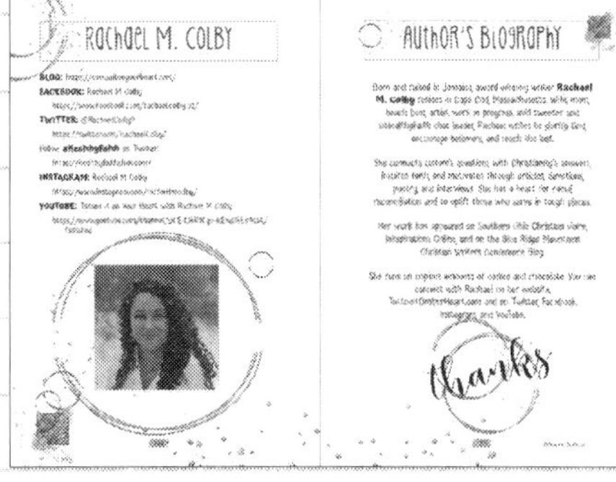

Author Biography & Contact Information

Organizing with Creativity & Color

The key to organizing is doing whatever works for you.
And adding a little color & creativity in the planning helps me.

- [ ] **1.** Use a color-coded key to indicate status and priority or type of project.
- [ ] **2.** Which colors provide visual emphasis and "at-a-glance" focus for you?
- [ ] **3.** Take time to gather your pens, tools, and colored pencils. List them.
- [ ] **4.** Choose 5-7 favorite colors or use the colors matching the cover art.
- [ ] **5.** Organizing uses the left side of the brain. Plan, order, numbering, listing, etc.
- [ ] **6.** Coloring uses the right side of the brain. Creativity, art, doodling, coloring, etc.
- [ ] **7.** Which type of left-brain tasks help you organize?
- [ ] **8.** Which type of right-brain activities help you enjoy organizing?
- [ ] **9.** How else can you help create a peaceful and productive home & work space?

List Favorite Poetry Forms & Styles

What forms of poetry are you familiar with? Make a list of forms you would like to study as you fill out this journal.

Su M T W T F Sa

lists & more lists

List Poetic Devices

Study a variety of poetic devices & list your favorites.

Have you tried alliteration? An abba rhyme scheme?

1. ☐ ____________________
2. ☐ ____________________
3. ☐ ____________________
4. ☐ ____________________
5. ☐ ____________________
6. ☐ ____________________
7. ☐ ____________________
8. ☐ ____________________
9. ☐ ____________________

Su M T W T F Sa

List Favorite Poets

List your favorite poets and writers. Read various styles of poetry.

Learn from the masters and try your hand at various forms.

Su M T W T F Sa

lists & more lists

POETRY IDEAS

References, Links, or Resources:

Use this space to add to your study.

How to write an ode:

https://www.writingbeginner.com/how-to-write-an-ode/

https://powerpoetry.org/resources/writing-ode-poem

Irregular Rhyming Ode

A tribute to a person, place, object, idea or event.

There is no strict line or stanza rules.

Something important to the poet.

Normally serious in nature.

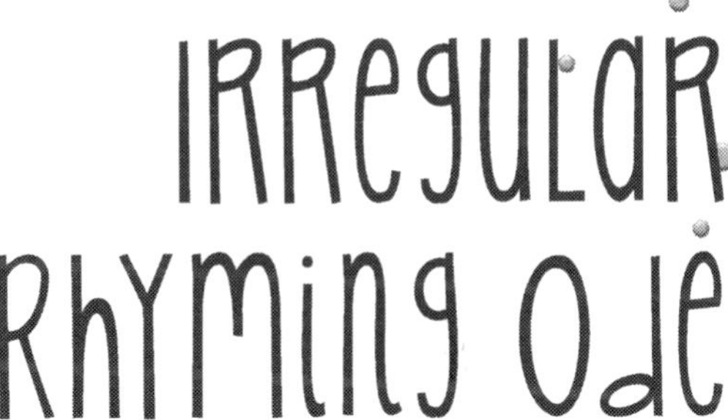

STRUCTURE OF AN ODE: 1. Strophe 2. Antistrophe 3. Epode

TYPES of ODES: 1. Pindaric 2. Horatian 3. Irregular

https://www.masterclass.com/articles/poetry-101-what-is-an-ode-poem-learn-about-the-3-different-types-of-ode-poems-with-examples#what-is-the-structure-of-an-ode-poem

Who inspires you?

Turn the page to create some art or poetry .

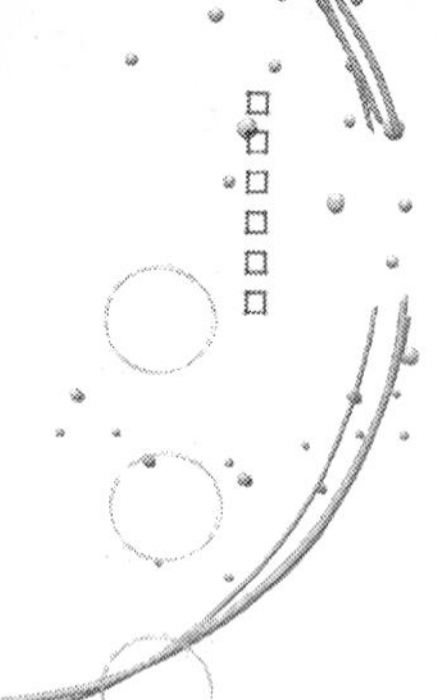

Poetry Inspiration

Ode to Nano

oh barren page
blank and white—
white and cold—
cold as night

oh waiting page
pen and ink—
ink won't flow—
flow nor think

oh battered page
curled and torn—
torn and stained—
stained and worn

oh happy page
filled and bright—
bright with words—
words of light

oh scribbled page
white or black–
black with thoughts–
thoughts fly back

oh count each page
all penned words–
words all count–
count all words

oh finished page
completed book–
book of love–
love it took!

~ Patricia Tiffany Morris

NaNoWriMo is National Writing Month
Online every November

Find an object—meaningful or of interest—and write down parts of this object. Personify that object of your affection by giving them human attribution.s.

Do you prefer handwriting, using a typewriter, or writing on a computer? Show your relationship, don't tell what you feel, and write without saying the words "feel" or "think."

What can you do the next time writer's block threatens to keep you from filling the pages of your journal? Make a list of ideas or journal about writer's block.

Describe a time when your words would not flow. Use colorful verbs and adjectives to bring life to your prose.

Poetry Ideas

References, Links, or Resources:

Use this space to add to your study or list rhyming words.

Here is a link to a family friendly resource:

https://www.familyfriendpoems.com/collection/short-free-verse-poems/

Another resource with 5 Tips for writing free verse.

https://powerpoetry.org/actions/5-tips-writing-free-verse-poem

These poems are based on Scripture and may or may not be free verse, but you can listen to some of them, also.

https://heavensinspirations.com/scripture-poetry.html

Free Verse

Sometimes called no form poetry.

No formal rules or patterns.

Turn the page to create some art or poetry .

Who inspires you?

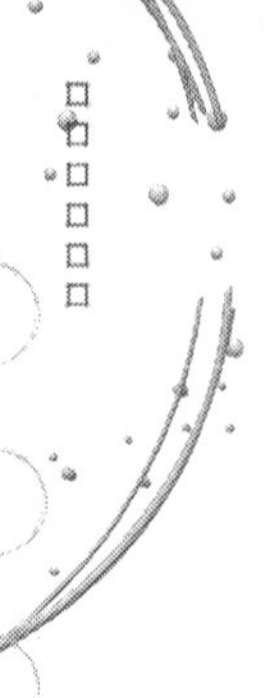

Poetry Inspiration

Untethered

Grief pierced unannounced,
And bleeding sap of sorrow dripped,
Smothering hacked scions of engagement.
The garden of the soul never fully tilled
For the dolor briars of the grave.

Two sprouts having sprung up together,
One remaining lone tendril
Lopped from the past,
Snipped from what could have been,
From a wasteland of shriveled ruins.

Tendrils wept vines of budding promise,
Dormant spores of grief
Severed the familiar from the future.
I was orphaned—unraveled and detached—
Separated from the haze of memory.

An antecedent belonging to a former time,
A "we" having withered into a "me,"
Vestiges of passed recollection
Lodged into me—alone—
The solitary carrier of the lot.

I felt abandoned.
Untethered.
And yet the Great Vine says
"I Am."

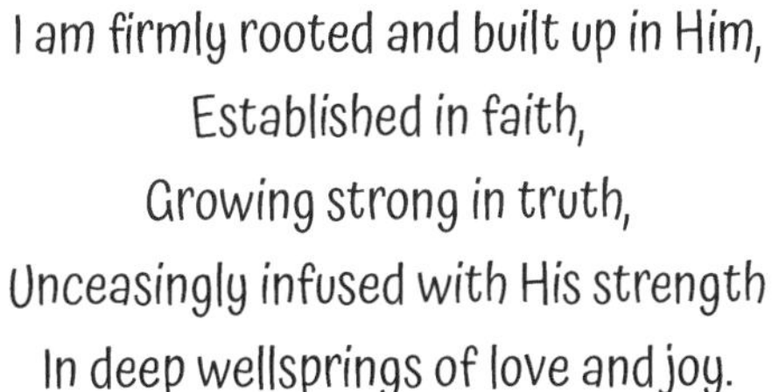

I am firmly rooted and built up in Him,
Established in faith,
Growing strong in truth,
Unceasingly infused with His strength
In deep wellsprings of love and joy.

I am a daughter of the King,
Flourishing in the shade of His presence,
Planted by the Tree of Life,
A living testimony of His goodness,
The apple of His eye, fastened, unmovable, held.

I am rich in blossoming hope,
Tendrils strengthened with His Spirit's power,
Dwelling in heavenly places through faith,
Never alone, always refreshed,
Abiding in deep wells of His Living Water.

And I am grafted into a new family of righteousness,
A "me" having merged into "we,"
Christ in me, the fullness of God,
The fruit of the Spirit blooming within,
The garden of the Living Lord.

Cherished.
Attached.
Tethered.

~ Aleisha Cate

Journal your reaction to the poem, Untethered. Write how you connected to the writer's thoughts and emotions. Do you feel tethered or untethered at this time in your life?

Have you ever felt abandoned or neglected or alone? Write about your feelings. How can you connect with others so they feel loved? How can you stay grounded in the Word of God?

Using free verse create a poem below. Think about a time someone gave you a gift or told you that you were special. Compare and contrast something in nature to personify feelings.

Think of ways you are rich. How does this value give meaning to your relationships? Journal about a time that lifted and encouraged you despite the negative circumstances.

Poetry Inspiration

Ideas for writing worship lyrics as poetry. https://worshipdeeper.com/183/how-to-write-a-worship-song/

"This is How to Write a Great Worship Song Every Time"

This website hosts popular song lyrics for you to study:

http://www.songlyrics.com/praise-and-worship-lyrics/

If you'd like to hear the song and several more worship songs written and sung by Terha Knittel, visit GODTUBE:

https://www.godtube.com/search/?q=Terha+Knittel

WORShiP SONG LYRICS

Sometimes similar to an Ode.

Sung to music.

Do you sing? Have you ever composed a song in your mind? What about the words of your prayers? Draw or sketch a shape and then fill the shape with words to remind you why you sing.

Turn the page to create some art or poetry .

Who Inspires You?

Poetry Inspiration

A Love Unfailing

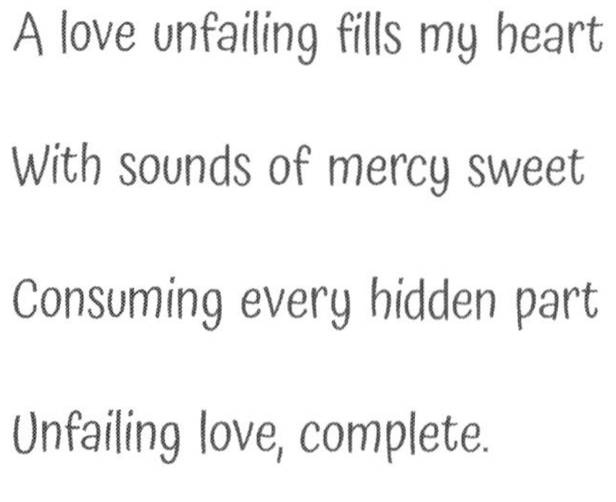

A love unfailing fills my heart
With sounds of mercy sweet
Consuming every hidden part
Unfailing love, complete.

Unfailing love has rescued me
Eternal love is mine
My soul once captive is set free
Unfailing love, divine.

Surround me with your love so pure
Consume me with your fire
O love unfailing, ever sure
My lifelong heart's desire.

Your love has cast my fear away
Your perfect peace is true
Your faithful love leads me each day
Lord, I will follow you.

~ Terha Knittel

Listen to this song on GODTUBE

https://www.godtube.com/search/?q=Terha+Knittel

Write a song in the space below. Use rhyme and a repeatable rhythm. Imagine the impact when the words are put to music.

Compose a worship song about a hope that will never fade. Let your song be a prayer to God. Add a refrain and repeat the message of your lyrics.

Poetry Ideas

References, Links, or Resources:

Use this space to add to your study or list rhyming words.

Visit this resource to find various poetry terms:

https://www.poetryfoundation.org/learn/glossary-terms/acrostic

A fun acrostic poem generator to spark the imagination:
A popular acrostic poem by Lewis Carroll is called "A Boat Beneath a Sunny Sky."
http://www.acrosticpoem.org

Write letters of a word vertically on your page.
Let the sentences and phrases tell a story
Or describe the word.

Consider the creative use of ABC's in poetry or children's picture books. Use several letters of the alphabet to describe God. Joy, Peace, Love, Truth, etc. Think of other acrostic poems you have read or research other poets.

Turn the page to create some art or poetry .

Who inspires you?

Triumph in Travail

How do I get through this challenge?
Over a hurdle that seems way too high?
Pain and despair threaten to conquer,
Ending my carefree days.

Run to the Father for comfort.
Invite the Spirit to speak.
Sing praises to help me feel hopeful.
Invest in time on my knees.
Never stop trusting the promise.
God's love is refining my dear.

~ Loretta Gjeltema

How does hope Rise in You?

Use the space below to write your reflection on hope rising despite trials.

H

O

P

E

R

I

S

I

N

G

Now it's your turn. Write an acrostic poem with any words you'd like. See the resources on the previous page for ideas.

Write other words to create more acrostic poems. Maybe you'd like to combine an acrostic poem with a crossword shape. Embellish the letters of the acrostic poem and color them.

Describe a time in your life when you suddenly faced great pain or loss. What did you see or hear? Did you notice a particular smell? Use all your senses to describe a trial or struggle. Then give the situation to God as a prayer.

What are some hurdles that make trusting God difficult in times of great trials? Journal about those thoughts of loss & grief or create a poem.

Poetry Ideas

References, Links, or Resources:

Use this space to add to your study or list rhyming words.

One of my favorite resources for poetry forms:
https://www.writersdigest.com/write-better-poetry/list-of-50-poetic-forms-for-poets "
List of 168 Poetic Forms for Poets" by Robert Lee Brewer

What emotions does the writer invoke in the next poem? Do you feel the anxiety and the hope? Create a list of emotions. Choose one or two and write free verse.

List of emotions that you'd like to explore in free verse:

Free Verse

Verse with no meter or rhyme or structure..

Emotional impact over structure.

Who inspires you to write? Write a poem to someone who encourages and uplifts.

Turn the page to create some art or poetry .

Who inspires you?

The Why of Why I Write

Why do I breathe?

Inhale.

Exhale.

Breathe.

How can I not?

It's in me.

It's who I am.

It's what He's called me to.

Sometimes it's how I speak to Him,

Praying on paper.

Sometimes it's how He answers me.

When He does, He tells me,

"Write this down."

Lest I forget.

So others may know Him

And not walk alone

So He may be glorified

When the going is good.

So He may be glorified

When life is bitter.

To give others hope.

Why do I write?

Because I must.

Breathe.

Pray.

Write.

~ Rachael M Colby

Take a few minutes to pray and seek God's direction!

How does God inspire you or show hope to others? What compels you to hope instead of despair? Write about a time when God brought you out of discouragement or depression.

Have you ever written a poem as a prayer? Organize your thoughts on this page and then turn those notes into a poem as a prayer to God.

Compose a poem of doubts and struggles in your call to write. Allow every other line to be God's rebuttal.

Why do you write? Pray about then write your mission statement and the vision God gave you for your writing.

Do you ever feel insufficient for the task of writing? Consider II Corinthians 3:5. Pray, find, and record a few scriptures to encourage you in your call.

Poetry Ideas

References, Links, or Resources:

Use this space to add to your study or list rhyming words.

Often called shape poetry or concrete poetry or a calligram. The poem 's subject becomes the shape for the poem.

http://www.shadowpoetry.com/resources/wip/shape.html

"Wiki How" has a website showing how to create shape poetry.

https://www.wikihow.com/Write-Shape-Poems

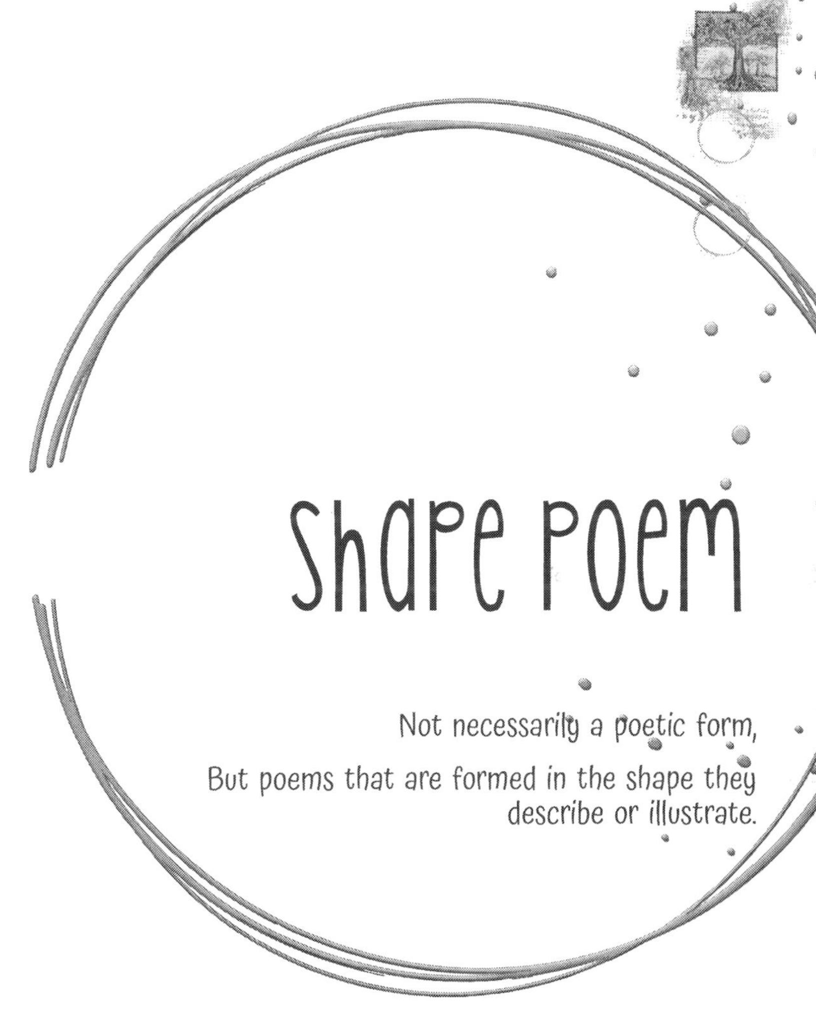

Shape Poem

Not necessarily a poetic form,

But poems that are formed in the shape they describe or illustrate.

How are shape poems different from free verse? What types of shapes might work to illustrate an idea? Sketch several shapes and ideas for each poem and brainstorm content, concepts, and ideas.

Who inspires you?

Turn the page to create some art or poetry .

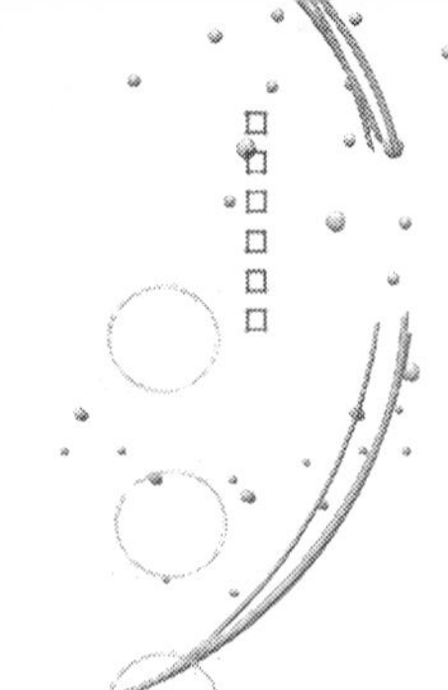

Poetry Inspiration

Song of Ascent

This ancient song of ascents
Precedes each step
And flows from my heart.

Climbing higher
The mountain of the Lord beckons me upward.

Journeying with song
To the One, Faithful and True.
My heart's satisfaction.

Joy meets my efforts,
Overflowing and bursting through the tug of earth.

Gratitude woven with every step,
I dance the dance of the redeemed
In the light of His radiance.

Love swirls encompassing each note and syllable.
Worship magnifying Him.
My heart is home.

~ Linda Heath

Imagine this version as one climbs a mountain.

This
ancient
song of ascents
precedes each step,
and flows from my heart.
Climbing higher, the mountain
of the Lord beckons me closer.
Journeying with song to the One,
Faithful and True, my heart's satisfaction.
Overflowing joy lifting me to burst through
the tug of earth. Gratitude woven with every
step, I dance the dance of the redeemed into the
light of His radiance. Love swirls, encompassing each
note and syllable. Worship magnifies Him. My heart is home.

Or in the shape of a mountain.

This
ancient
song of ascents
precedes each step,
and flows from my heart.
Climbing higher, the mountain
of the Lord beckons me closer.
Journeying with song to the One,
Faithful and True, my heart's satisfaction.
Overflowing joy lifting me to burst through
the tug of earth. Gratitude woven with every
Step, I dance the dance of the redeemed into the
light of His radiance. Love swirls, encompassing each
note and syllable. Worship magnifies Him. My heart is home.

NOTE: Adjustments to your poetry and word order might be needed to fill the intended shape.

In this song of ascent the writer conveys a journey to a mountain. Explore the use of literal and metaphorical or figurative journeys. How is our praise like climbing a mountain?

Choose a shape & expand the concept on the next two pages. Let your words dance on the page and fill the space with breath as you convey the emotions and meaning.

Can you draw a path of a highway, or road and sketch a poem about traveling? Use a scratch piece of paper to get the form and ideas flowing and then transfer to this page.

Try a door and fill the space with a poem. Don't worry about line breaks or where the words fall. Just fill with words. Think varying letter widths & even different letter styles.

POETRY IDEAS

References, Links, or Resources:

Use this space to add to your study or list rhyming words.

Here is a resource on reverse poetry:

https://theeducatorsroom.com/reverse-poetry/

His is a fun list of examples of reverse poems:
http://poets.spice.org.hk/index.php

Reading these poems forward is a pessimistic view.

Reading them backwards is an optimistic viewpoint.

"The Pen and the Pad" website has a wonderful exercise:

https://penandthepad.com/write-reverse-poem-8556361.html

Reverse Poem

Poems that read both forward and backwards
Double meaning depending on which direction
The poem is read. Use opposite meanings.

Think of a concept that has opposing viewpoints or emotions.

You might find a template online that helps you organize your thoughts and ideas before trying to write the poem.

Who inspires you?

Turn the page to create some art or poetry .

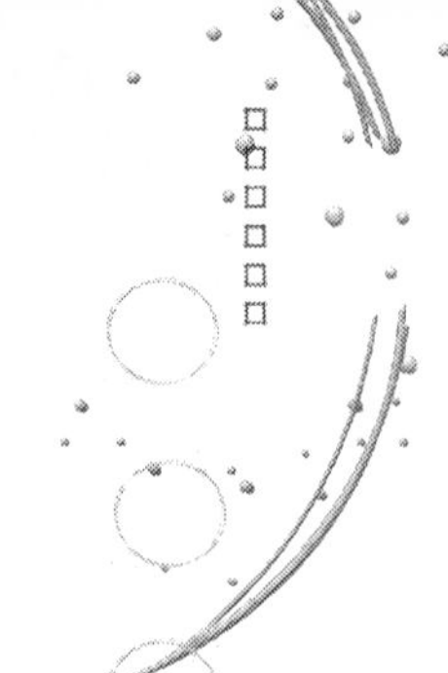

Poetry Inspiration

Unmasked

despair
sinks all
the vacant hollow sounds
relentless without
joy
hammering to find peace
and pleas of
lost opportunities
find sorrow
with words unmasked
screaming cries
sees an end
the pain
still and silent
a graveyard
echoing inside
a restless mind
without
hope

hope
without
a restless mind
echoing inside
a graveyard
still and silent
the pain
sees an end
screaming cries
with words unmasked
find sorrow
lost opportunities
and pleas of
hammering to find peace
joy
relentless without
the vacant hollow sounds
sinks all
despair

~ Patricia Tiffany Morris

Poem written forwards and backwards

Make a list of opposite concepts that might work well for a reverse poem.

Find a template and transpose the structure in the space below. Or write a positive message and then write the opposite message beside the first.

Write or journal about hope vs despair. Choose to meditate on hope and let the writing about thoughts of despair lead toward the hope that believers have in Christ.

Journal about fear on the top half of this page. And then write about courage on the lower half of the page. How are they alike? How are they different?

Choose two opposite emotions and journal your thoughts to turn the inspiration into a reverse poem or allow the exercise to express your feelings.

Poetry Ideas

References, Links, or Resources:

Use this space to add to your study or list rhyming words.

What is the difference between free verse and blank verse?

https://www.masterclass.com/articles/poetry-101-what-is-the-difference-between-blank-verse-and-free-verse

What is alliteration? Can you identify this poetic device in Rachael's poem called Ramshackle Soul?

https://literarydevices.net/alliteration/

Free Verse

Focus on emotional connection to reader
Generally no recognizable form or style.
No meter, or rhyme or metrical form.

Choose a subject to write or journal. Composing a poem is a very personal journey. What subjects keep you up at night? What thoughts could use some exploration and examination?

Who inspires you?

Turn the page to create some art or poetry .

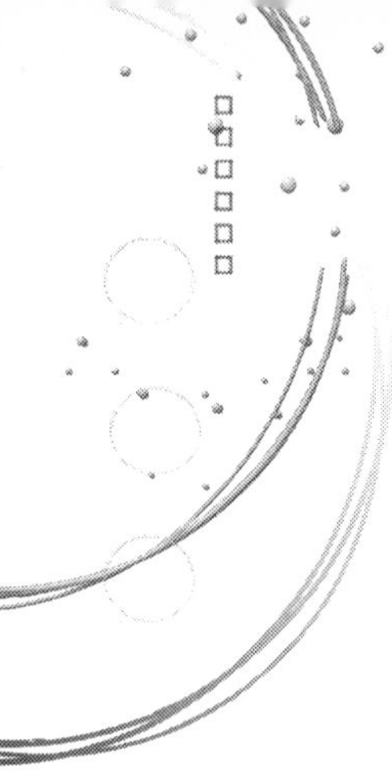

Ramshackle Soul

The King has ransomed
my ramshackle soul

I was lost and languishing
A wayward wanderer
He bought me and brought me in
I come boldly before His throne
I am adopted and adored
He turns my sorrow into song
My pain into praise

I know the heart-healer
He holds my hand

I know the mind-mender

He makes broken into beautiful

I know the storm-stiller

He stirs my soul

The Prince of Peace

Is redeemer and re-maker

Savior and sanctifier

Steadfast sustainer

My heart is the castle of the King

~ Rachael M Colby

Adoption is a powerful statement of choice. Did you know you were adopted by the King of Kings? God chose you to be His child. Write what comes to mind when you contemplate this.

How has your relationship with God changed over the past few years? Write thoughts and phrases of praise and turn them into a psalm.

Use this page to write word combinations such as mind-mender, heart-healer, to express in alliteration characteristics of God or of people you know or characters you read and write about.

Try a poem with an intro, a middle, and an ending. Start with a problem. In the middle write what happened—the story. End with the conclusion or a message of the poem.

Poetry Ideas

References, Links, or Resources:

Use this space to add to your study or list rhyming words.

Describe or define an Ode? What are the parameters? How do you write an ode?

https://www.writingbeginner.com/how-to-write-an-ode/

List examples of odes. Keats, for example, wrote a style all his own.
https://examples.yourdictionary.com/poetry-examples-of-odes.html

There are many rhyming references online. Here is one of my favorite websites:

https://rhymer.com

Lyrical verse with a passionate expression.

Regular or irregular meter or rhythm.

Pays tribute to a person or subject.

Turn the page to create some art or poetry .

Who inspires you?

The Hope of God's Eternal Way

Our churches may stand empty
But our hearts incline toward You.
We cry out for revival,
For changed lives and minds anew.

Teach us to surrender
The swelling fear within our soul.
We release a wealth of worry
To Christ's powerful control.

Oh, Lord, would you have mercy
Upon the prodigal we pray.
Call each one to your side,
Every wandering, errant stray.

Release in us your gifts
To preach and teach and share.
Both friend and steadfast foe
Witness Jesus' love and care.

Neither the events of night
Nor pestilence of day
Steals the hope in Jesus Christ–
Our God's eternal way.

~ Tammy Kennington

Similar to song lyrics, this poem shares a rhyming pattern and 4-line stanzas.

hope

Love

Sketch words of hope.

Tammy Kennington

Notice the stanzas with 4 lines each. The second and 4th lines of each group of 4 lines rhyme. Write a poem that employs ending rhyme.

Write a question and then turn it into a dialogue in the form of free verse using ending rhyming words, double rhymes, or internal rhyming words.

Describe how your relationships were affected over the past year. Consider relationships with Christ, self, family, and friends. Journal your thoughts and feelings.

Reflect on spiritual needs for yourself or for our world today. Create a poem with rhyming words that speaks to our need for love, acceptance, and spiritual and mental health.

POETRY IDEAS

References, Links, or Resources:

Use this space to add to your study or list rhyming words.

List some of your favorite free verse poems.

List your favorite poets. What style do they write?

List topics for exploration in free verse style.

Free Verse

Writing without rhyme, rhythm or meter.
Focus on the emotions and a theme.

Turn the page to create some art or poetry .

Who inspires you?

Inside Out

The front door's red paint peels, reveals a season of life
ten years ago, when I thought doors should be painted gray.
I used to welcome strangers
friends now standing at a distance
shouting through the glass. And I
screaming within to hide away.

Spackled nail-holes crusted beige, weighs today's choices
preparing to sell our home with neutral hues
over yesterday's eggplant kitchen walls.
I used to paint our house with
pumpkin and grape, hanging lemon tea towels
beside cranberry-lime and drapes of blues.

Capturing more than diffused light or frequent spills
the memory of those who willed these gifts.
We live in covered boxes
waiting for the next place
we'll call home. Packing up pieces
and memories of home and of life's rifts.

Weeds pulled from the dirt lay weeping
and withered bricks cry for us to follow their way.
　　Gathering prayers for new owners
　　clearing the path for a fresh start
　　for them—for us. Growing strong
　　through the trials we weather today.

I'll miss this place. The red door.
The brightly painted walls within and garden walls without
welcoming friends into our home—our lives.
Yesterday, today, and tomorrow.

Tomorrow we'll start again.
Hopeful within.
And without.

~ Patricia Tiffany Morris

Describe using specifics and named items how your environment can reflect the poet's inner attitudes and perspective. Use color, familiar objects, and actions to mirror internal angst.

Compare and contrast the "before & after" of a situation that caused or allowed change. Journal your experiences and the consequences of action or inaction.

Journal about how the weather affects you and mirrors a circumstance in the present or the past. Think about how the weather could personify emotions?

Think of a memory where you felt hopeful and filled with a positive attitude. Write about it. How can you reflect on this experience when you feel discouraged and alone?

Poetry Ideas

References, Links, or Resources:

Use this space to add to your study or list rhyming words.

Research Limericks - Rhyming pattern of AABBA

https://kingoflimericks.com/serious-limericks-there-once-was-an-unsmiling-rhymer/

Humorous metered form is a poem of exactly 5 lines. The 1st, 2nd and 5th lines rhyme and have anywhere from 7-10 syllables. The 3rd and 4th lines rhyme and have 5-7 syllables. Each set has the same rhythm. See examples on the internet.

Linda's syllable structure is 9-9-5-5-9. Did you know that the number of syllables can vary a little? Research this form online. Create a limerick.

Rhythm of da-da-DUM da-da-DUM da-da-DUM is often called the Dr. Seuss meter. Although normally humorous, try writing a serious limerick.

Enter "The Saturday Evening Post" limerick contests. Check your state poetry society & join for more opportunities.

Limerick

Limericks are usually silly or humorous

Structure: 5 lines with an AABBA rhyming pattern.

Even though the next poet created a serious poem, try writing some silly responses to a problem.

Limericks are traditionally humorous and silly. Sometimes quite effective, serious or sober reflections of life help us heal. Read both the sad truth expressed in Linda's poem, and then the levity from the poem by Patricia. Serious events happen. How we handle them can help us heal.

Who inspires you?

Turn the page to create some art or poetry .

Poetry Inspiration

From Sad to Glad

Now there once was a girl who was sad.
She was frightened and hurt by her dad.
But learned to forgive,
To break out and live,
From the fear and the sad to the glad.

- Linda Heath

Writing Rad Becomes a Fad

Now it's said there's a girl who was rad.
She fights lies with a pen and a pad.
Telling stories for sport,
Sharing tales with a snort,
And the dad jokes became all the fad.

- Patricia Tiffany Morris

SAD DAD GLAD RAD PAD FAD

Use this space to write about a time you were hurt. Give that hurt to God and let the healing words flow.

Forgive ...
And Live.

Brainstorm ideas for limericks. The content and style are meant to be humorous, but let your imagination create a story and keep this list for creative Ideas for other types of poems.

Ideas & Themes

- [ ]
- [ ]
- [ ]
- [ ]
- [ ]
- [ ]
- [ ]
- [ ]
- [ ]
- [ ]
- [ ]
- [ ]
- [ ]
- [ ]
- [ ]
- [ ]

Write about a time when you were frightened or ashamed. How can you forgive others or God to break free from guilt & shame? How does hope in Christ help us heal?

POetRY IDEAS

References, Links, or Resources:

Use this space to add to your study or list rhyming words.

List themes for your next free verse poem.

Compare free verse with blank verse and prose. Write any structure or no structure.

3-syllable words:

4-syllables words:

5-syllables words:

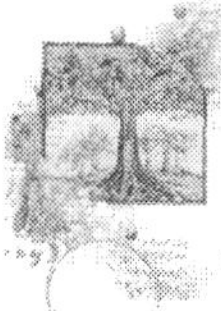

Free Verse

Find a theme and write from the heart.

Create a list of 3-5 syllable words. Find synonyms and collect them for a future poem. Start with fathomless and infinite and write synonyms and antonyms. Add to your list the character qualities of God.

Turn the page to create some art or poetry .

Fathomless

Why do we let our finite problems eclipse our infinite God?
Why do we limit the possibilities
When we have access to a limitless God?
He is unsearchable
Yet He calls us to know Him
The more I know Him
The less I feel I know
He is fathomless
He is all encompassing goodness and grace
I never tire of Him
He occupies my mind
He is my Savior
He is winner and ruler of my heart
Rescuer and lover of my soul
I have tasted the wine of His Word and will
And I want all of Him
Nothing else satisfies
Nothing ever will

~ Rachael M Colby

Take a few minutes to pray & ask God to help you know Him more fully.

Write a love letter in the space below.

Notice the grounding nature of the content. "I am" and "He is" are repeated and emphasized. List other words suitable as anchors in your life. Write an "I am" about yourself.

The variation of sentence length gives a breath from line to line. How else can you describe God's character? Journal with varying line and sentence length to add interest.

Do you struggle to embrace God's ability and willingness to move on your behalf? List three Bible verses that counter this thought pattern. Journal your thoughts.

Reflect how God overcame a situation for you which seemed insurmountable. Write how He solved the dilemma. Express your gratitude for increasing your faith in His faithfulness.

POETRY IDEAS

References, Links, or Resources:

Use this space to add to your study or list rhyming words.

Online tool for finding various rhyming words: End rhyme, beginning rhymes, double rhymes, triple rhymes, last syllable rhymes, first syllable rhymes. https://rhymer.com

https://www.wordhippo.com/what-is/words-that-rhyme-with/words.html

Rhymes, synonyms, antonyms and more.

Rhyming Verse

A poem with a structured rhyming pattern.

Turn the page to create some art or poetry .

Who inspires you?

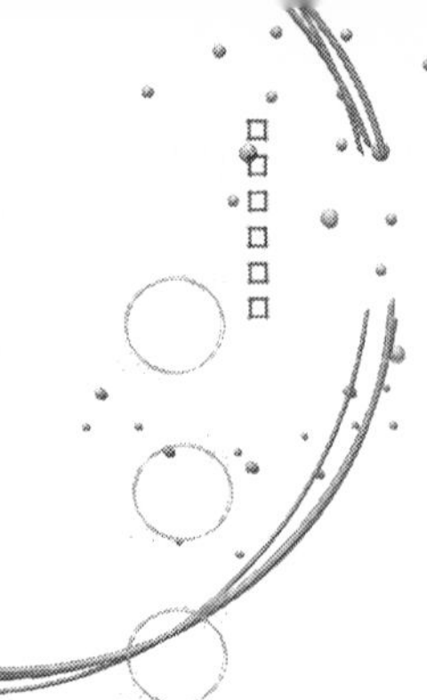

Creative a Symphony

Writers often fight the block.
They pen the words to speak.
Artists seldom paint with fear.
They dream of worlds we seek.

Poets whisper beats and sounds.
They carve and syncopate.
Dancers shape a message pure.
They weave and contemplate.

Words and pictures capture hope.
They help us to rejoice.
Celebrate in holy song,
For those who have no voice.

Poets, artists, dancers be,
Writers in a symphony.

~ Patricia Tiffany Morris

Who inspires you to hope? Who speaks for you when the world seems bleak? Journal rhyming sentences you might use for a poem on the next few pages.

Journal about someone or a group who needs an advocate. Perhaps you can mail the poem as a reminder of their importance in this world.

A symphony brings to mind collaboration and working together in harmony. Write about a collaboration with musical terms and artistic word choices.

POETRY IDEAS

References, Links, or Resources:

Use this space to add to your study or list rhyming words.

Ekphrastic Poetry is poetry inspired by a work of art or photography. It is a visual writing prompt. It is a commentary on a visual piece of work.

Here are some famous Ekphrastic poems:

https://interestingliterature.com/2019/11/ekphrasis-poems-paintings-examples/

One of my favorite Ekphrastic writing challenges comes from The Ekphrastic Review. https://www.ekphrastic.net/ekphrastic-writing-challenges/ekphrastic-challenge-responses-lily-prigioniero

Ekphrastic Poetry

A pictorial inspiration for a poem or prose.
Writing inspired by visual composition.

The following Ekphrastic poem by Delta Jane Holte is based on the famous tree that grew around an abandoned bike. You can find photos online at https://www.adventure-journal.com/2018/05/the-daily-bike-july-10-2012-2/

Turn the page to create some art or poetry .

Who inspires you?

Poetry Inspiration

Relationships Through Time

One day a bicycle was abandoned, but by whom,

the tree did not know.

Heartbroken, Bicycle wept in despair.

swooping low with his branches, Tree embraced her.

The two formed an unbreakable bond.

Abandonment and loneliness dissipated

to mere whispers of the past.

As the years stretched on,

Tree continued to grow next to his dear friend.

Passers-by laughed and joked at the sight of them,

unable to recognize or understand

the deep relationship that rested there.

~ Delta Jane Holte

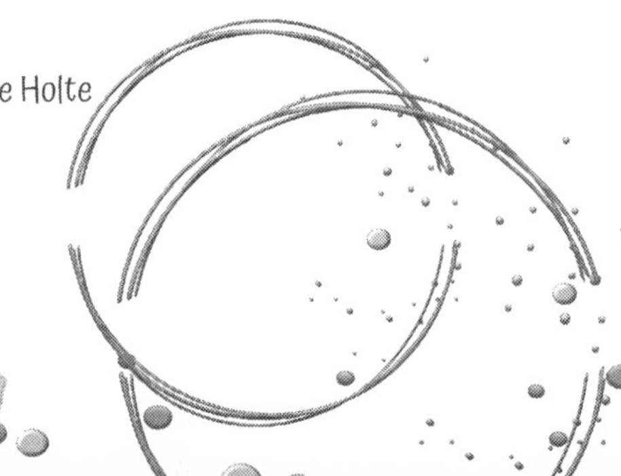

Journal about a relationship that stands the test of time.

Choose a favorite painter and compose an Ekphrastic poem inspired by the work of the artist, or the artist's life.

Personification is a powerful tool. Re-read the poem and notice how the tree and the bicycle are written with human emotions. Try that technique and create prose poetry.

Journal about an unbreakable bond you have with a friend or family member. What makes such a relationship strong?

Write about the first friendship you can remember from childhood. What made it memorable and special? What elements of friendship can you bring to new relationships?

Poetry Exercise

Have you ever written a post or a journal entry and wondered if you could transpose your writing into prose or a poem? Take a look at this exercise and examine the ideas for creating a new art form.

Original Journal Entry and Social Media Post

How I would love to find a place that emanated such peaceful calm, with cool hues of blue and soft greens surrounding me...a place to reflect. Finding such a place allows me to delve deep into the secret places of my heart, but I ask myself, "am I bold enough to face what might be hidden there?" Be it treasure or turbulence, I am not yet ready, so I turn my attention to bright citrusy treats that remind me of the brilliant and bold flavours of summer...ooh...and the juicy escapades that await me in the coming days. Can I allow myself such adventure and possibilities? Change can be a struggle even in the most positive circumstances - am I strong enough to withstand even the slightest delight? For now, here in a blessed oasis of momentary calm I face a blank, sun-soaked page. Perhaps the most adventure filled possibilities await me on the tip of my pencil.

- Delta Jane Holte

PROSE WRITING EXERCISE

This section is a collaboration between two writers.
The first portion is a paragraph writing prompt.
The next page is a reformat of the paragraph
On the facing page to the left.

Be Courageous. Be Bold.
Let Hope Rise Within
and Heal You by the Tip of Your Pencil!

Turn the page to create some art or poetry .

Who Inspires You?

The Tip of My Pencil

to find a place—a place of love—
emanating peaceful calm reflecting hues
of coral blues against a sea of greens
surrounding me—a place to rest—and to reflect
on finding such a place—a resting home
to delve within and dive
into secret places of my heart—my home

am I bold enough or strong enough
to face what might be hidden there
treasure fair or turbulence
wait for change the struggle grows
and I'm not ready yet—not yet

my attention turns my focus drifts
to brilliant citrus treats
the bold flavours of the summer waves
and juicy escapades await
the coming days arrive and rise
in ripening adventure
and struggles wash the shores
in waves and being brave enough

but am I strong enough to withstand
the slightest sure delight or success
a blessed oasis in this rest
a momentary calm
I face a blank and sun-soaked page
perhaps adventure waits
adventure-filled with possibilities all mine
on the tip of my pencil

~ Delta Jane Holte and Patricia Tiffany Morris

Journal about finding adventure when you write. How does writing present possibilities beyond the physical journey?

Journal about a place you'd like to travel if you had enough time and money. Notice visual elements, sounds, smells, and anything that draws readers into your adventures.

Use this space to plan your next journal.

A Collection of Notebooks, Journals, Logbooks, & Planners for Creativity & Organization

find your style

look for greeting cards of the cover artwork and special offers.

www.patriciatiffanymorris.com

thanks

oh, the people i've met

A special thanks to my endearing husband who offers his humor, puns, encouragement, and keen poetic insights.

To Terha Knittel, lovely composer and vocalist extraordinaire, who composed the music in the video promotions and for my book trailers.

To Kyle Knittel who guided me through many hours of video production.

To Erica Alexander who formatted my original 3D covers.

To Rachael Colby who spent long hours reminding me that I can't give up.

To Elaine Giles and the MacBytes crew for teaching me about Affinity software, Scrivener, and many, many tech tricks.

To KG Fonts and FontSpring for the stress free licenses.

To my launch team and FB group who helped proofread, edit, and cheer me toward and through publication. My gratitude to these idea generators, amazing brainstorming networkers, and the many cheerleaders, formatting ninjas, and "let-it-be-enough" believers, trust soldiers, and prayer warriors.

Thank you for blessing my proverbial socks off!

to the One who created all things and for His glory.

Aleisha Cate

WEBSITE: https://www.shelivesingrace.com

EMAIL: leish22@comcast.net

FACEBOOK: She Lives in Grace

FB URL: https://facebook.com/GraceunLEISHed

INSTAGRAM: https://www.instagram.com/graceunleished

Author's Biography

Aleisha Cate loves to share God's grace found in Jesus Christ.

She lives in Michigan and is a wife to her amazing husband and a mother to four wonderful boys. Her husband jokes he would hate to be one of her perennials because she moves them around so much!

When she is not hanging with her family, writing her first book, playing the piano, or talking to her garden plants, you can often find her in a coffee house sipping tea with a friend.

She would love to chat with you, too!

Rachael M. Colby

BLOG: https://tattooitonyourheart.com/

FACEBOOK: Rachael M Colby

https://www.facebook.com/rachael.colby.92/

TWITTER: @RachaelColby7

https://twitter.com/RachaelColby7

Follow **#HealthyFaith** on Twitter:

https://healthyfaithchat.com/

INSTAGRAM: Rachael M Colby

https://www.instagram.com/rachaelmcolby/

YOUTUBE: Tattoo it on Your Heart with Rachael M Colby

https://www.youtube.com/channel/UCE-fJkR1Cgu-KEnq74EqAQA/featured

Author's Biography

Born and raised in Jamaica, award-winning writer **Rachael M. Colby** resides in Cape Cod, Massachusetts. Wife, mom, beach bum, artist, work in progress, avid tweeter and #HealthyFaith chat leader, Rachael writes to glorify God, encourage believers, and reach the lost.

She connects culture's questions with Christianity's answers, inspires faith, and motivates through articles, devotions, poetry, and interviews. She has a heart for racial reconciliation and to uplift those who serve in tough places.

Her work has appeared on Southern Ohio Christian Voice, Inkspirations Online, and on the Blue Ridge Mountains Christian Writers Conference Blog.

She runs on copious amounts of coffee and chocolate. You can connect with Rachael on her website, TattooItOnYourHeart.com and on Twitter, Facebook, Instagram, and YouTube.

Loretta Gjeltema

WEBSITE: www.LorettaGjeltema

INSTAGRAM: https://www.instagram.com/lorettagjeltema

TWITTER: https://twitter.com/LorettaGjeltema

Author's Biography

Loretta Gjeltema is a teacher at heart who encourages women to thrive as they engage with God's Word.

She writes devotionals, leads the Tuesday Ladies Bible Study, and mentors younger women. She blogs at at LorettaGjeltema.com and writes regularly as a team member at the "Balanced and Beautiful in Christ" Facebook group.

Current projects include a Christmas devotional book and a devotional for women.

Loretta's desire is to bring Scripture to life through the retelling of Biblical stories.

Linda Heath

TRAVEL & FOOD BLOG:

https://buchatrek.blogspot.com/

FACEBOOK AUTHOR PAGE:

https://www.facebook.com/Linda-Heath-Scribe-104919371863602

INSTAGRAM: https://www.instagram.com/buchatrek/

Author's Biography

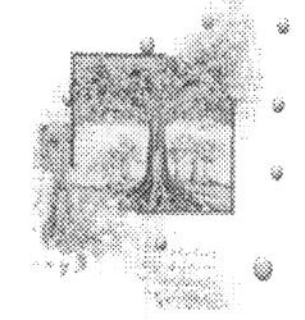

Enjoying the freedom of retirement, **Linda Heath** and her husband Jerry are snowbirds. They live and travel in a 38-foot RV. Drawn south by the Arizona winter sunshine where they wander from place to place, and they return in the summer, parking near Olympia, WA.

Summers are a treasured time to spend with their two kids and six grandchildren. She enjoys passing on some of the skills she's developed to the next generation, like playing piano, ukulele, and recorder as well as sewing, painting and fiber arts. Dressing up in Grandma's jewelry, much of which she made, is a favorite activity with the littles.

2020 framed the year she started writing seriously and found her tribe in the writing community. Having started a blog to share travels with family, it has now expanded to include both a food journey as well as a spiritual journey. Other projects are in the works.

Delta Jane Holte

FACEBOOK: https://www.facebook.com/delta.holte

Author's Biography

Delta Jane Holte is a licensed practical nurse in British Columbia, Canada.

Growing up, she lived in an imaginary land of stories, where characters and plot lines emerged and flowed out through the tip of her pencil.

In 2020, Delta was published in not one, but two anthologies: "The Christ Collective" and "Beneath the Mask: Hope, Faith, and Transformation in the Midst of COVID-19," achieving her lifelong dream of becoming a published author.

Tammy Kennington

WEBSITE: www.tammykennington.com
INSTAGRAM: https://www.instagram.com/tammylkennington
MEWE: https://www.mewe.com/i/tammykennington1
MEWE GROUP: Conquering the Giants Trauma Recovery
TWITTER: https://twitter.com/TammyKennington
LINKEDIN: https://www.linkedin.com/in/tammykennington/
FACEBOOK: https://www.facebook.com/tammylkennington
TIKTOK: https://www.tiktok.com/@tammykennington2

Author's Biography

Tammy Kennington is a writer and speaker familiar with the impact of trauma, mental health issues, and parenting in the hard places. Her desire is to lead women from hardship to hope and to share the love of Christ with the young and young at heart. She speaks at churches and conferences nationwide, including mom's groups and women's retreats as well as secular organizations such as schools and community groups.

Her love for writing began at eight years old, when she penned her first poem. Spurred by its early publication in the Rural Montana magazine, Tammy dreamed of authoring books. Now an award-winning writer, she has been featured in numerous publications including Crosswalk.com, AriseDaily.com, Refresh Magazine, and MOPS.

Her desire to inspire other women led Tammy to pursue certification as a life coach. She also holds a Master's in Teaching, a Bachelor of Arts in Elementary Education, a certificate in the Foundations of Trauma, and recognition as a Certified Academic Language Therapist. Having served in education for over twenty years, Tammy helps remediate students with dyslexia and finds special joy investing in children.

She is married to her high school sweetheart, Dave, and is the mother of two young adults, and two teens. She's the proud dog-mom to Dandy, an eighty-pound lap puppy. In her free time, Tammy enjoys reading and sipping a warm mug of Earl Grey.

Terha Knittel

GODTUBE: https://www.godtube.com/search/?q=Terha+Knittel

INSTAGRAM: https://www.instagram.com/tsknittel/

Author's Biography

Having spent the first 20 years of her life in Southern Illinois, **Terha Knittel** spent the following ten years living in Dallas, Tx and then Lancaster, Pa before returning to Southern Illinois where she met her husband.

After her marriage, the couple moved to Tennessee where Terha continued her education at Carson Newman University and earned a Music degree with a concentration in Religion.

For the past 24 years she has resided in Augusta, GA, enjoying family, new experiences online, and worshipping and creating music.

The Knittels have one biological daughter, one adopted son from Ukraine, and two sons and a daughter adopted from Russia. You will find her musical compositions at GodTube.

Patricia Tiffany Morris

WEBSITE: https://www.patriciatiffanymorris.com

PINTEREST: https://www.pinterest.com/patriciatiffanymorris/

FACEBOOK: https://www.facebook.com/PatriciaTiffanyMorris

TIKTOK: https://www.tiktok.com/@journalingscribbles

TWITTER: https://twitter.com/PatTiffanyInks

IG WRITER: https://www.instagram.com/PatriciaTiffanyMorrisWriter/

FB WRITER PAGE: https://www.facebook.com/PatTiffanyInks

LINKEDIN: https://www.linkedin.com/in/patricia-tiffany-morris

ETSY SHOP: https://www.etsy.com/shop/TiffanyInksStudio

YOUTUBE: https://www.youtube.com/c/PatriciaTiffanyMorris

Author's Biography

An incorrigible writer, passionate artist, and eclectic creative, **Patricia Tiffany Morris** sketches ideas in her sleep, that is when she takes time to sleep. All night reading and studying served her well during architectural design studio at ISU in the eighties where she soaked up engineering and computer skills.

Now an empty-nester, she's inspired by her rhyming husband, who reads her suspense-filled fiction in delightful character voices and helps her brainstorm plot threads. She adores Pinterest and hashtags, but finds Twitter quirky.

Patricia actively supports fellow authors and offers geeky tech services for a minimal price. Tiffany Inks Studio LLC began in 2021 and sells the branded JOURNALING SCRIBBLES™, a collection of artsy journals, notebooks, and planners.

Her goal to share Christ through inspirational fictional stories brought her numerous awards from 2019-2021 in poetry, short fiction, children's stories, and suspense fiction, including 1st place at BRMCWC for her upcoming split-time novel. Her publishing credits include The Ekphrastic Review, Word Weavers Int, and Guideposts among other places including a collection of Journaling Scribbles™ journals, notebooks, and organizers.

thanks

journaling scribbles™

A Collection of Journals, Notebooks, Logbooks, and Planners for Creativity & Organization

Which one will you choose next?

Each book fits into one of 9 different color-coded categories.
Some journals have a variety of cover options.

Future editions and versions will be marked on the front cover.

Categories:

1 planners
2 Writing
3 Spiritual Life
4 Family & Friends
5 House & Things
6 adventures
7 Creativity
8 Projects & Activities
9 wellness

creativity & organization

Tiffany Inks Studio LLC

Journaling Scribbles™ Collection

creativity *journals* for writers

what will you write next?

Guided Journal Writing Prompts for an Additional 30 days:

1-2	I'm a child of God wrapped in a blanket of courage and faith.
3-4	I'm an eclectic creative, spinning patterns of joy.
5-6	I'm an artist woven in textures of beauty & hope.
7-8	I'm a song of direction, ordering steps, like the notes on a page, or words left to right.
9-10	I'm a puzzle, putting pieces together & solving mysteries.
11-12	I'm a networking ninja, making intentional connections.
13-14	I'm a gardener planting seeds and growing flowers.
15-16	I'm an architect and builder, building strong foundations.
17-18	I'm a prayer warrior, falling on my knees and lifting prayers to God.
19-20	I'm brainstormer, mapping ideas to problems and finding solutions.
21-22	I'm a writer, discipling and cultivating grace.
23-24	I'm no one, and yet, I'm enough.
25-26	I'm set apart for His glory alone.
27-28	Thank you, Lord, for your salvation.
29-30	Thank you, Lord, for giving me breath.

please know that i am praying for you.

I'd love to hear from you. If you have a journal page to share with me, find me on social media at

Tag me on IG @PatriciaTiffanyMorris or on FB @TiffanyInksStudio

Made in the USA
Coppell, TX
20 March 2023

14471011R00088